I HAVE A NEWS

RHYMES FROM THE CARIBBEAN

Collected by Walter Jekyll

ILLUSTRATED BY JACQUELINE MAIR

Chosen with a note on the rhymes by Neil Philip

Albion

For Emily, with love

An Albion Book

First published in Great Britain in 1994 by
The Albion Press Ltd, Spring Hill, Idbury, Oxfordshire OX7 6RU

Distributed by Melia Publishing Services
P.O. Box 1639, Maidenhead, Berks SL6 6YZ

Designer: Emma Bradford
Project Manager: Elizabeth Wilkes

Illustrations copyright © Jacqueline Mair 1994
Volume copyright © The Albion Press Ltd 1994

The rhymes in this book were originally published in
Walter Jekyll *Jamaican Song and Story*, 1907.

A CIP catalogue record for this book is available from the British Library.

ISBN 1 871927 09 9

Typesetting by York House Typographic, London
Printed and bound in Italy by New Interlitho

CONTENTS

ME COCK A CROW

Me cock a crow
Coo-coo-ri-co
Before day him a crow
Coo-coo-ri-co
Him a crow fe me wake
Coo-coo-ri-co.

RISE A ROOF

Rise a roof in the morning,
Rise a roof in the morning;
Tell all the people them to come, come, come,
Rise a roof in the morning.
The Monkey and the Baboon them was sitting on the wall,
Rise a roof in the morning;
I an' my wife cannot agree,
Rise a roof in the morning
She spread me bed on the dirty floor,
Rise a roof in the morning
For Devil made the woman an' God made man,
Rise a roof in the morning.

DOWN TOWN GAL

Down town gal no have no water
To wash them head to keep them clean.
Down town gal no have no water
To wash them head to keep them clean.
Down town gal no have no water
To wash them head to keep them clean.

Why! Why! Why!
Take them gal in charge
Why! Why! Why! Policeman
Take them gal in charge.

THERE'S A BLACK BOY IN A RING

There's a black boy in a ring, tra la la la la,
There's a black boy in a ring, tra la la la la,
There's a black boy in a ring, tra la la la la,
He like sugar and I like plum.

Wheel an' take you pardner, jump shamador!
Wheel an' take you pardner, jump shamador!
Wheel an' take you pardner, jump shamador!
For he like sugar an' I like plum.

TOADY, TOADY

Toady, Toady, min' you'self,
Min' you'self make I plant me corn;
Plant me corn fe fo plant me peas,
Plant me peas fe fo court me gal,
Court me gal fe fo show mumma,
Mumma de one a go tell me yes,
Puppa de one a go tell me no;
Toady, Toady, min' you'self,
Min' you'self make I plant me corn.

ALL THEM GAL A RIDE

All them gal a ride merry-go-round,
Me no see no gal like a dem ya.
Ride him, ride him, ride him, ride him,
Ride him round the town,
Ride him, ride him, ride him, ride him,
Ride him round the town.

MERRY GO ROUND

Merry go round a go fall down,
Fall down, fall down,
Merry go round a go fall down
Sake a de worthless rider.
Rider, rider, try to sit down good
Rider, rider, try to sit down good
Rider, rider, try to sit down good
Merry go round a go fall down.

COMPLAIN COMPLAIN

Complain complain complain,
Complain about me one,
Me daddy complain, me mammy complain,
Complain about me one.

I HAVE A NEWS

I have a news to tell you all about the Mowitahl men;
Time is harder ev'ry day and harder yet to come.
They made a dance on Friday night an' failed to pay the drummer,
Say that they all was need of money to buy up their August pork.
Don't let them go free, drummer! Don't let them go free, drummer!
For your finger cost money to tickle the poor goat-skin.
Not if the pork even purchase self, take it away for your labour,
For your finger cost money to tickle the poor goat-skin.

MISS NANCY RAY

Oh Miss Nancy Ray, oh hurrah boys!
Oh Miss Nancy Ray, oh hurrah boys!
Nancy Banana da broke man heart,
Oh hurrah boys!
Nancy Banana da broke man heart,
Oh hurrah boys!
Oh Miss Nancy Ray, oh hurrah boys!
Oh Miss Nancy Ray, oh hurrah boys!

ME AN' KATIE NO 'GREE

Me an' Katie no 'gree,
Katie wash me shirt in a sea.
If you t'ink a lie,
If you t'ink a lie,
Look in a Katie eye.

LITTLE SALLY WATER

Little Sally Water sprinkle in the saucer;
Rise Sally, rise an' wipe your weeping eyes.
Sally turn to the East, Sally turn to the West,
Sally turn to the very one you like the best.

On the carpet you must be
Happy as the grass bird on the tree.

Rise an' stand up on your leg
An' choose the one that you like the best.
Now you married, I give you joy,
First a gal an' second a boy;
Seven year after, seven year to come,
Give her a kiss an' send her out.

OLD MOTHER PHOEBE

Old mother Phoebe, how happy you be
When you sit under the jiniper tree,
Oh the jiniper tree so sweet.
Take this old hat an' keep you head warm,
Three or four kisses will do you no harm,
It will do a great good fe you.

A NOTE ON THE RHYMES

The Jamaican folk rhymes in this book were all collected by one man, Walter Jekyll. They were, he tells us, "taken down from the mouths of men and boys" in the Port Royal Mountains behind Kingston and included in his book *Jamaican Song and Story: Annancy Stories, Digging Sings, Ring Tunes, and Dancing Tunes,* first published in 1907. It was Jekyll's love for Jamaica and the Jamaicans that prompted him to record these rough and ready rhymes, which were improvised and varied according to the moment.

Some of the rhymes, such as "I Have a News," are very local: gossip set to a dance tune. This one describes the scandalous nonpayment of a drummer hired for the traditional August merrymaking at Mowitt Hall. Some, such as "Miss Nancy Ray" and "Toady, Toady," are work songs. Others, such as "Little Sally Water," are free adaptations of play rhymes known to generations of British and American children. Alice B. Gomme's *The Traditional Games of England, Scotland, and Ireland* (1894–98) included forty-eight versions of this rhyme; William Wells Newell's *Games and Songs of American Children* (1883) also noted it; and it is still played today.

"Little Sally Water" was so popular in Jamaica that its title became a general term for ring games. Jekyll vividly described one version of the game: "The boys and girls join hands and form a ring. One—the sex is immaterial—crouches in the middle and personates Sally Water. At the words 'Rise, Sally, rise,' he or she slowly rises to an erect position, brushing away imaginary tears, turns first one way and then another, and chooses a partner out of the ring. Where the tempo changes, they wheel—a rapid turning dance—and after the wheeling, the partner is left inside the ring and becomes Sally Water."

The tunes for the rhymes, given at the end of this book, were improvised, and varied in much the same way as the words. Often borrowed from chanteys and hymns, they were given particular charm by their rhythmic organization. Jekyll compared Jamaican rhythms with ragtime syncopation: The first beat in each bar is exactly midway between the first and second beats of common measure. This sense of beating *against* time is still characteristic of Jamaican music today.

Work songs and dance songs had been recorded in Jamaica before Jekyll; some of the best can be found in Paula Burnett's *The Penguin Book of Caribbean Verse in English* (1986). Later collectors have added to Jekyll's store, notably Martha Warren Beckwith in her *Jamaican Folklore* (1928). Beckwith's book has, for instance, variant versions of "Little Sally Water" and "There's a Black Boy in a Ring." Her text for the latter reads "brown gal," as in the version made into an international hit by the pop group Boney M. in 1978. But no one has supplanted Walter Jekyll's rich harvest of Jamaican rhymes.

The rhythms and idioms of these verses echo in the work of such contemporary Caribbean poets as John Agard, Louise Bennett, Grace Nichols, Marlene Philip, and Andrew Salkey. James Berry's *When I Dance* (1988) contains a lovely reworking of "Toady, Toady." In the work of such writers, the music of these rhymes rings out still.

Neil Philip

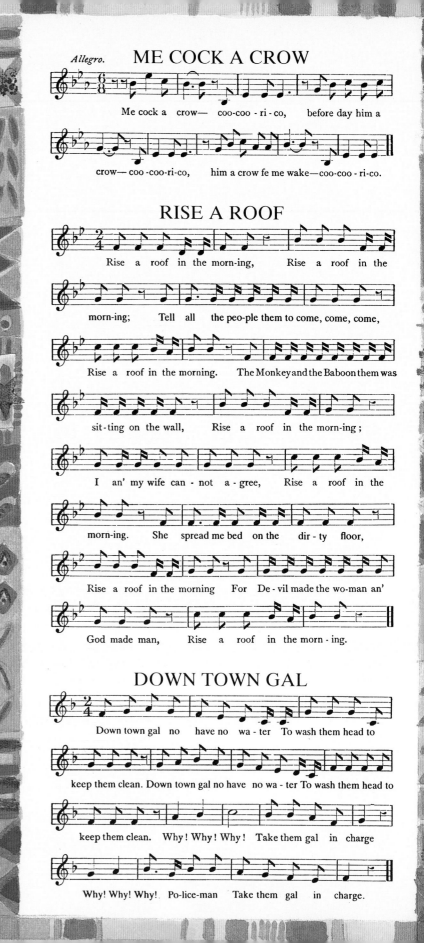

THERE'S A BLACK BOY IN A RING

Allegro.

There's a black boy in a ring, tra la la la la, There's a black boy in a ring, tra la la la la, There's a black boy in a ring, tra la la la la, He like su - gar an' I like plum.

Wheel an' take you pard - ner, jump sha - ma - dor!

Wheel an' take you pard - ner, jump sha - ma - dor!

Wheel an' take you pard - ner, jump sha - ma - dor! For

he like su - gar an' I like plum.

TOADY, TOADY

Vivace.

Toa - dy, Toa - dy, min' you - 'self Min' you - 'self make I

plant me corn; Plant me corn fe fo plant me peas,

Plant me peas fe fo court me gal, Court me gal fe fo

show mum-ma, Mum-ma de one a go tell me yes, Pup-

pa de one a go tell me no; Toa - dy, Toa - dy,

min' you - 'self, Min' you - 'self make I plant me corn.

ALL THEM GAL A RIDE

All them gal a ride merry-go-round, Me no see no gal like a

dem ya. Ride him, ride him, ride him, ride him,

Ride him round the town, Ride him, ride him,

ride him, ride him, Ride him round the town.

MERRY GO ROUND

Mer - ry - go-round a go fall down, Fall down, fall down,

Mer - ry - go - round a go fall down Sake a de worth-less

ri - der. Ri - der, ri - der, try to sit down good

Ri - der, ri - der, try to sit down good Ri - der, ri - der,

try to sit down good Mer - ry - go-round a go fall down.

COMPLAIN COMPLAIN

Complain complain complain, Complain a - bout me one, Me

daddy complain, me mammy complain, Complain about me one.

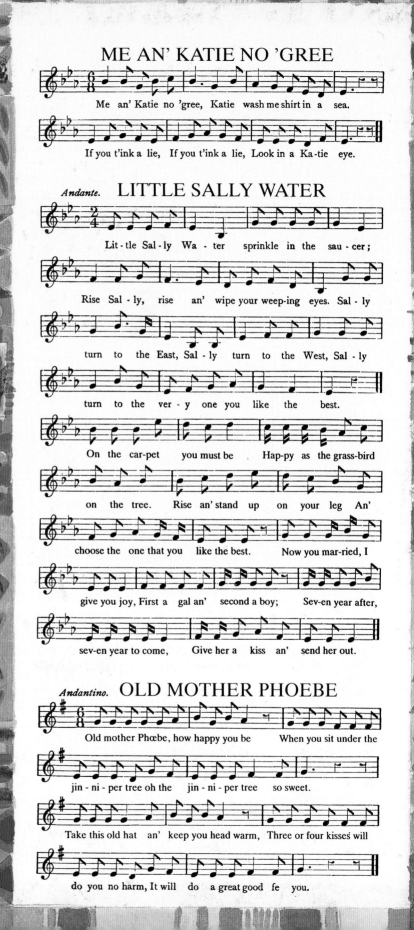

I HAVE A NEWS

I have a news to tell you all a - bout the Mowitahl

men; Time is harder ev -'ry day and harder yet to

come. They made a dance on Fri - day night an' failed to pay the

drummer, Say that they all was need of money to

buy up their August pork. Don't let them go free, drummer!

Don't let them go free, drummer! For your fin-ger cost money to

tick - le the poor goat -skin Not if the pork ev - en

purchase self, take it away for your labour, For your finger

cost money to tick - le the poor goat - skin.

MISS NANCY RAY

Allegro.

Oh Miss Nancy Ray, oh hur-rah boys! Oh Miss Nancy Ray,

oh hur-rah boys! Nancy Banana da broke man heart, Oh hurrah boys!

Nancy Banana da broke man heart, Oh hurrah boys! O Miss Nancy Ray,

Oh hur - rah boys! Oh Miss Nan-cy Ray, oh hur - rah boys!

ME AN' KATIE NO 'GREE

Me an' Katie no 'gree, Katie wash me shirt in a sea.

If you t'ink a lie, If you t'ink a lie, Look in a Ka-tie eye.

LITTLE SALLY WATER

Andante.

Lit - tle Sal - ly Wa - ter sprinkle in the sau - cer;

Rise Sal - ly, rise an' wipe your weep-ing eyes. Sal - ly

turn to the East, Sal - ly turn to the West, Sal - ly

turn to the ver - y one you like the best.

On the car-pet you must be Hap-py as the grass-bird

on the tree. Rise an' stand up on your leg An'

choose the one that you like the best. Now you mar-ried, I

give you joy, First a gal an' second a boy; Sev-en year after,

sev-en year to come, Give her a kiss an' send her out.

OLD MOTHER PHOEBE

Andantino.

Old mother Phœbe, how happy you be When you sit under the

jin - ni - per tree oh the jin - ni - per tree so sweet.

Take this old hat an' keep you head warm, Three or four kisses will

do you no harm, It will do a great good fe you.